# Make it Easy

## Age 8-9

## English

## Contents

**Alison Head and Louis Fidge**

# Speaking and listening (1)

Interviewing someone is a great way to see if you can listen carefully and remember what was said – it's fun, too!

**1** Interview a relative who is older than you about what it was like when they went to school. Plan some questions to ask them, using the words in the box to help you.

a _What is it like in School?_

b _How was lunchtime?_

c _What lessons did you learn?_

d _Where your teachers good?_

e _Did you do P.E?_

> lunchtime
>
> games
>
> assembly
>
> homework
>
> lessons
>
> PE
>
> teachers
>
> uniform

**2** Can you remember what they said? Write an account of what you remember below. Was their school very similar or different to your experiences?

_Slietly because Somethings they do like myns somethings they don't._

# Homophones

Homophones are words that **sound the same**, but have **different meanings** or **spellings**.

You need to think about the whole sentence to know which is the right word to use.

flour          flower

We bought some **flour** to bake the cake.

I picked a red **flower**.

**1** Write homophones for these words.

a knew _____ nell _____
b hole _____ whole _____
c grate _____ great _____
d there _____ ther _____
e two _____ too _____

f herd _____ heard _____
g sea _____ see _____
h be _____ bee _____
i for _____ four _____
j write _____ right _____

**2** Write a sentence for each word to show you know how to use it correctly.

a plaice _____ We had plaice and chips. _____
b place _____ I know the place you mean. _____
c threw _____ I threw a ball. _____
d through _____ I went through a Jungle _____
e son _____ hi Son _____
f sun _____ The Sun is realy bright _____
g floor _____ The floor is clean _____
h flaw _____ I got the flaw _____
i main _____ I went on the main floor on a tolter _____
j mane _____ There is the mane _____

3

# Verb endings

Verbs tell us what a person or thing is **doing**. The ending of the verb changes depending on **who** is doing the activity and whether it has already happened (past), is happening now (present) or will happen (future).

*she walk**ed**     she walk**s**     she will be walk**ing***

Sometimes the spelling of the verb changes when the ending is added.

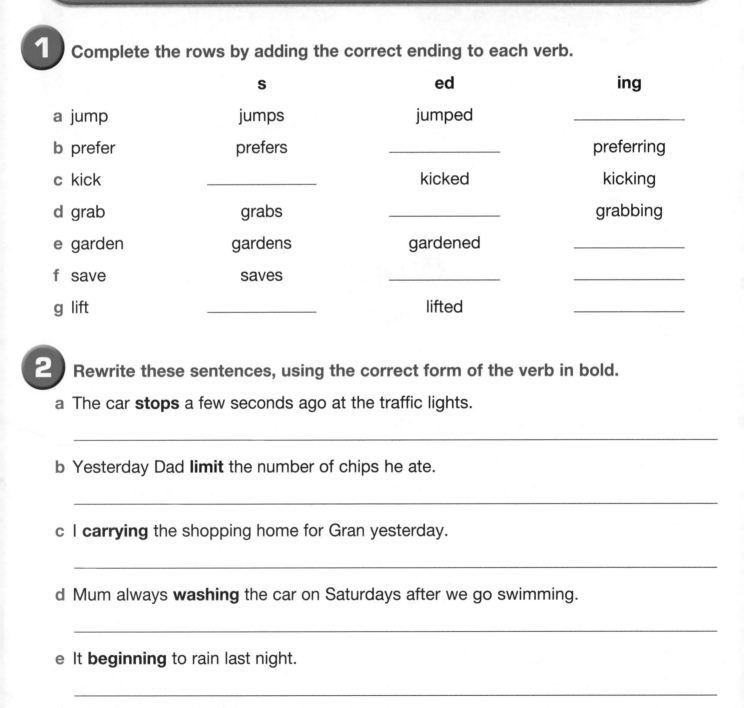

**1** Complete the rows by adding the correct ending to each verb.

|  | s | ed | ing |
|---|---|---|---|
| a jump | jumps | jumped | _____ |
| b prefer | prefers | _____ | preferring |
| c kick | _____ | kicked | kicking |
| d grab | grabs | _____ | grabbing |
| e garden | gardens | gardened | _____ |
| f save | saves | _____ | _____ |
| g lift | _____ | lifted | _____ |

**2** Rewrite these sentences, using the correct form of the verb in bold.

a The car **stops** a few seconds ago at the traffic lights.

_____

b Yesterday Dad **limit** the number of chips he ate.

_____

c I **carrying** the shopping home for Gran yesterday.

_____

d Mum always **washing** the car on Saturdays after we go swimming.

_____

e It **beginning** to rain last night.

_____

f Jenny always **exploring** the rock pools as soon as she gets to the beach.

_____

# Suffixes *ship*, *ness* and *ment*

We can add suffixes to the **ends** of some words to change their meaning.

*Ship*, *ness* and *ment* are suffixes which do not change the spelling of the root word.

sponsor + **ship** = sponsorship

fair + **ness** = fairness

battle + **ment** = battlement

The only exception is if the word ends in a consonant followed by *y*, when you change the *y* to *i* before adding the suffix.

tid**y** + **ness** = tid**i**ness

**1** Complete these word sums.

a  merry + ment = _____

b  kind + ness = _____

c  fit + ness = _____

d  enjoy + ment = *enjoyment*

e  lazy + ness = *lazyness*

f  member + ship = *membership*

g  silly + ness = *Sillyness*

h  friend + ship = *freindship*

i  careless + ness = *Carelessness*

j  happy + ness = *happyness*

**2** Choose *ship*, *ness* or *ment* to add to each of these words. Then write down the new word.

a  measure _____

b  tidy _____

c  nasty _____

d  employ _____

e  state _____

f  wicked _____

g  fellow _____

h  apprentice _____

i  replace _____

j  champion _____

## Speaking and listening (2)

Giving spoken or oral reports is a great way to practise speaking clearly and confidently. Spoken reviews are another good way to make sure you can organise ideas, and report them orally.

**1** Give a spoken review of your favourite film to a grown-up.

a What is the title of your favourite film?

_____

b Who is your favourite character, and why?

_____

c What, in your opinion, is the most exciting thing that happens in the film?

_____

d How do you feel about the ending? Does it resolve any problems that arose during the story?

_____

**2** Make notes to help you plan a spoken report about an exciting day out.

a Where did you go, and why?

_____

b What transport did you use to get there? Was it far? How long did it take?

_____

c Describe what happened during the day.

_____

d Would you want to go again if you got the chance? Give reasons for your answer.

_____

e Would you recommend the day out to a friend?

_____

# Alphabetical order

Putting words in alphabetical order helps us to find information in **dictionaries** and **indexes**.

If the first two letters of a group of words are the same, we can use the third and fourth letters to put the words in alphabetical order.

baby

baggage

ball

a **b** c d e f **g** h i j k **l** m n o p q r s t u v w x y z

**1** Use the third bold letter to find each word in the box. Then write the missing letters so the words are in alphabetical order. The first one has been done for you.

| sunny super suspect submarine sudden |
| summer sugar suitable success |

a su**b**marine

d sug_____

g sun_____

b su**c**_____

e sui_____

h sup_____

c su**d**_____

f sum_____

i sus_____

**2** Write these words in alphabetical order, using the third and fourth letters.

| hair hare hat hail |
| harp hard haste have |

a _____

e _____

b _____

f _____

c _____

g _____

d _____

h _____

# Adverbs

Adverbs tell us **how** a person or thing does something.

I walked **quickly** to school.

The fish swam **energetically**.

**1** Complete the word sums to spell these adverbs correctly.

a complete + ly = _____

b comic + ly = _____

c usual + ly = _____

d sleepy + ly = _____

e bad + ly = _____

f total + ly = _____

g humble + ly = _____

h basic + ly = _____

i gentle + ly = _____

**2** Think of a suitable adverb to complete these sentences. Write your adverb.

a The mouse scurried _____ away.

b My sister stormed _____ from the room.

c Gemma thought _____ about the maths problem.

d The star shone _____ in the sky.

e Liam dawdled _____ home.

f Jess _____ scribbled down the phone number.

g My naughty brother behaved _____.

h Dad patted the dog _____.

i We talked _____ in the library.

# Making verbs

We can turn some nouns and adjectives into verbs by adding **suffixes** like *ate, en, ify* or *ise*.

With most words you can just add the suffix. If the word already has a suffix, or ends in *e* or *y*, the suffix or final letter must usually be removed before you add the new suffix.

deaf + **en** = deafen

quantity – **ity** = quant

quant + **ify** = quantify

**1** Complete these word sums to make new verbs.

a deep + en =  _____

b short + en =  _____

c standard + ise = _____

d apology + ise = _____

e note + ify =  _____

f elastic + ate =  _____

g pure + ify =  _____

h formal + ise =  _____

i wake + en =  _____

j medic + ate =  _____

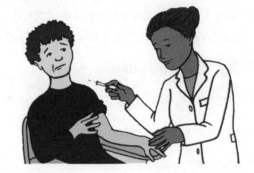

**2** Add *ate, en, ify* or *ise* to these words to make verbs.

a intense _____

b real _____

c strength _____

d simple _____

e hard _____

f glory _____

g haste _____

h class _____

i serial _____

j weak _____

# Irregular verbs

When verbs are used to tell us what a person or thing has already done, most end in *ed*. This is called the past tense.

**Present**
I **look** at the book.

**Past**
Yesterday I look**ed** at the book.

Some verbs have their own spelling patterns, especially in the past tense. These are known as irregular verbs.

I **keep** rabbits.          I **kept** rabbits.

**1** These past tense verbs are wrongly spelt. Write them correctly.

a I hurted my hand. _____

b Sam putted his toys away. _____

c Claire runned home. _____

d Mum bringed my tea. _____

e I sended you a letter. _____

f The autumn leaves falled from the trees. _____

**2** Rewrite these sentences, starting with the words in bold. Make sure you spell the past tense verbs correctly. The first one has been done for you.

a I eat my birthday cake.

**Yesterday,** I ate my birthday cake.

b Jamilla buys a comic.

**Last week,** _____

c Ali draws a picture.

**Earlier today,** _____

d I am tired.

**Last night,** _____

e I can swim.

**When I was four,** _____

f I tell you a secret.

**Yesterday,** _____

# Commas

Commas show us when to **pause** in a sentence.

They are also useful for **breaking up** longer sentences.

Which is your coat, Alex?

Jo, my friend, is eight years old.

**1** **Add the missing commas to these sentences.**

a After tea we played football.

b Find your trainers Paul.

c Suddenly the lights went out.

d Judy and James from next door came shopping with us.

e My hat which is black matches my scarf.

f Last Tuesday after school I went skating.

**2** **Rewrite these sentences, putting the commas in the correct place.**

a Tomorrow we, are playing football.

_____

b The ink which, was blue stained, the carpet.

_____

c Eventually Jane, won the game.

_____

d It's, time to go Ali.

_____

e While we were on, holiday we stayed in a hotel.

_____

f At, school in my classroom is a display about, trains.

_____

# Powerful verbs

Verbs tell us what a person or thing is **doing**.

The dog **runs**.

Powerful verbs also tell us **how** a person or thing does something. Sometimes they tell us so much, we do not need adverbs.

The dog **runs quickly**.

The dog **sprints**.

**1** Sort each verb in the box into its correct group. Then add one more suitable verb of your own to each group.

| hobbles argues devours munches shuffles dictates chews declares ambles |
| --- |

| walks | says | eats |
| --- | --- | --- |
| a _____ | b _____ | c _____ |
| _____ | _____ | _____ |
| _____ | _____ | _____ |
| _____ | _____ | _____ |

**2** Read the fairytale. Then choose a powerful verb from the box to use instead of the verbs and adverbs in brackets.

Jack and his mother were very poor. One day, Jack's mother (sternly told) _____ him to sell their cow. When he sold it for a handful of beans, Jack's mother (shouted loudly) _____ at him.

Overnight, a magic beanstalk (grew rapidly) _____ up into the clouds. Jack (climbed quickly) _____ to the top and (walked quietly) _____ past the sleeping giant.

As Jack (looked longingly) _____ at some bags of gold, the giant woke up, so he (quickly collected) _____ the gold and (ran away) _____ down the beanstalk.

When he reached the bottom, Jack's mother (cut quickly) _____ away at the beanstalk. The giant (fell heavily) _____ to the ground, and Jack and his mother lived happily ever after.

grabbed

shot

ordered

crashed

yelled

clambered

fled

hacked

gazed

crept

# Fronted adverbials

An adverbial is a word or phrase used like an adverb. Adverbs –
and adverbials – add information or details to verbs. Adverbials
explain **where**, **how** or **when** something happens.

He ate his dinner **after the sun went down.**

verb

adverbial

Fronted adverbials are words and phrases at the
**beginning** of a sentence, used to describe the action
that follows. Fronted adverbials are usually followed by a comma.

**After the sun went down,** he ate his dinner.

fronted adverbial

**1** Draw a line to match each fronted adverbial to the most sensible
sentence ending.

a Before the sun rose,                    he watched the stars.

b In front of the baker's                 I'll make lots of festive cakes and biscuits.

c All night long,                          he packed his bags.

d Before Christmas,                        he waited for his lunch.

e Under a blanket of leaves,              she watched out of the window.

f As quickly as he could,                 the hedgehog slept.

g All day,                                 she ate her breakfast.

**2** Write a fronted adverbial for these sentence endings. Don't forget to put a
comma after the fronted adverbial!

a _____ she watched television.

b _____ he waited for his friends.

c _____ the cat meowed.

d _____ the woman giggled.

e _____ the man climbed.

f _____ they wondered.

g _____ she walked away.

# Expressing time, place and cause

We can express time, place and cause in a sentence using conjunctions, adverbs and prepositions.

**Conjunction**

I went home **after** school.

**Adverb**

**Soon**, I shall go on holiday!

**Preposition**

I fell asleep **during** the afternoon.

**1** Underline the preposition, adverb or conjunction that expresses time.

a Can you hold this while I eat please?

b I went to the shops before work.

c I went to the park after school.

d It will be home time soon, children.

e I ate popcorn during the film.

**2** Write a sentence using each of these words.

a therefore _____

b when _____

c before _____

d soon _____

e during _____

f because _____

g after _____

# Tricky plurals

Plural means **more than one** of something.

When you spell plurals, there are rules you have to follow.

Words ending in *f* usually change to *ves* in the plural.

Words ending *ff* just add *s*.

leaf      lea**ves**      cu**ff**      cu**ffs**

**1** Underline the correct plural spelling for each word.

a **sniff**      snives    snifs    sniffs

b **half**      halves    halfs    halffs

c **puff**      puves    pufs    puffs

d **cliff**      clifs    clives    cliffs

e **scarf**      scarves    scarfs    scuves

f **scuff**      scufs    scuffs    scuves

g **calf**      calves    calfs    calffs

h **thief**      thiefs    thieves    thiefes

i **yourself**      yourselfs    yourselves    yourselff

j **knife**      knifes    kniffes    knives

**2** Write the plural form of these words.

a loaf   _____

b self   _____

c sheriff   _____

d cuff   _____

e wolf   _____

f wife   _____

g bluff   _____

h shelf   _____

i elf   _____

j scoff   _____

# Choosing words

Choosing the right words for your writing is important.

Some words don't tell us very much.

*We had a **good** time at the party.*

Other words are more powerful and tell us much more.

*We had a **fantastic** time at the party.*

**1** Draw a line to match each word with a more interesting alternative. The first one has been done for you.

| a | hungry | hilarious |
|---|--------|-----------|
| b | tired | terrifying |
| c | nice | parched |
| d | nasty | horrible |
| e | scary | starving |
| f | dry | lovely |
| g | wet | exhausted |
| h | funny | drenched |

**2** Rewrite these sentences, choosing a better word to replace the words in bold.

a It is **hot** today.

_____

b We **got** some crisps at the shop.

_____

c Kate **made** some biscuits.

_____

d The mouse was **small**.

_____

e We had lunch and **then** we went to the cinema.

_____

## Expanded noun phrases

Expanded noun phrases add **interest** to your writing by giving more **information** and **descriptions**. Expansion can happen both before and after the noun.

The monster roared. ➡️ The **scaly** monster, **with long dripping fangs**, roared.

**1** Rewrite these sentences to make them more exciting by using expanded noun phrases.

a The cat jumped.

_____

b The wind blew.

_____

c A rabbit hopped up the lane.

_____

d My mum laughed.

_____

**2** Write a sentence about each of these nouns. Use expanded noun phrases to make things exciting for your reader.

a bat _____

b kitten _____

c ghost _____

d woman _____

e fairy _____

f ship _____

g badger _____

# Making adjectives

Adjectives **describe** things or people. We can often make adjectives by adding a suffix to a noun or verb.

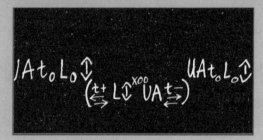

bore + ing = bor**ing**

Words ending in a single *e* drop the *e* when adding *ing* or *able*.

beauty + ful = beauti**ful**

Words ending in *y* change the *y* to *i* when adding *ful* or *able*.

**1** Complete these word sums to turn these nouns and verbs into adjectives.

a  shock + ing =  _____

b  wash + able =  _____

c  trust + worthy = _____

d  beauty + ful =  _____

e  rely + able  =  _____

f  acid + ic =  _____

g  road + worthy = _____

h  amuse + ing =  _____

i  break + able =  _____

j  pain + ful =  _____

**2** Choose *ful* or *able* to make adjectives. Then write the new words.

a  wish + _____ = _____

b  agree + _____ = _____

c  envy + _____ = _____

d  hope + _____ = _____

e  wonder + _____ = _____

f  care + _____ =  _____

g  adore + _____ = _____

h  help + _____ =  _____

i  value + _____ = _____

j  mercy + _____ = _____

# More adjectives

Adjectives can help us to compare things or people.

**Comparative adjectives** compare two things – *bigger*, *smaller*.

Kate's cat is **bigger** than mine.

**Superlative adjectives** describe the limit of a quality – *biggest*, *smallest*, *most enormous*.

But Mina's cat is the **biggest** of all.

**1** Decide whether the adjective in each sentence is comparative or superlative. Then tick the correct box.

|   | | comparative | superlative |
|---|---|---|---|
| a | This winter is the coldest on record. | ☐ | ☐ |
| b | I live closer to the school than you do. | ☐ | ☐ |
| c | I chose the least difficult question. | ☐ | ☐ |
| d | My sister is younger than me. | ☐ | ☐ |
| e | We saw the longest snake at the zoo. | ☐ | ☐ |
| f | Diamonds are more valuable than pearls. | ☐ | ☐ |
| g | My house is bigger than yours. | ☐ | ☐ |
| h | The theme park was the most exciting place I've ever been. | ☐ | ☐ |

**2** Complete the rows with comparative and superlative adjectives.

|   | comparative adjectives | superlative adjectives |
|---|---|---|
| a | taller | _____ |
| b | _____ | narrowest |
| c | more amazing | _____ |
| d | _____ | best |
| e | older | _____ |
| f | _____ | most delicious |
| g | stranger | _____ |
| h | _____ | least interesting |

# Apostrophes for contraction

If two words are used together a lot, we can sometimes join them together. We do this by taking out some of the letters and putting an apostrophe in their place.

do not → don't

I am → I'm

**1** Circle the incorrect contractions.

a **It's Its'** my birthday tomorrow.

b Jake is off school today because **hes he's** ill.

c I **didn't did'nt** do my homework.

d Unless we hurry **wel'l we'll** miss the bus.

e Dad **wo'nt won't** be home until later.

f My brother **wouldn't would'nt** let me watch TV.

g **You're Your're** my best friend.

h **Theyve They've** forgotten their bags.

**2** Rewrite these sentences, replacing the bold words with a contraction.

a We **must not** speak in class.

_____

b You can play football after **you have** done your homework.

_____

c He **should not** have eaten so much cake.

_____

d I **cannot** ice skate very well.

_____

e They **could not** find our house.

_____

# More apostrophes

Possessive apostrophes are used to tell us when something **belongs** to somebody or something.

With single or collective nouns, the apostrophe usually goes before the *s*.

With plurals ending in *s*, the apostrophe usually goes after the *s*.

The people**'s** shoes   The man**'s** hat   The girl**s'** bags

**1** Write the missing apostrophes in these phrases.

a the womans bag

b the boys heads

c the childs toy

d the peoples books

e two dogs baskets

f the suns rays

g three footballers boots

h a cats tail

**2** Write down the shortened form of each phrase. The first one has been done for you.

a the wings of a bird      *a bird's wings*

b the pens belonging to the boys    _____

c the cat belonging to Kim    _____

d the parcels belonging to Sam    _____

e the car belonging to my parents    _____

f the rattles belonging to the babies    _____

g the wallet belonging to my dad    _____

h the sweets belonging to the children    _____

# More suffixes

Sometimes you can add two suffixes to the end of a word.

> hope + **ful** + **ly** = hopefully

Sometimes you can add more than one different suffix to a word.

> relate + **ion** = relation
>
> relate + **ive** = relative

**1** Complete these word sums. Remember the spelling rules for adding suffixes.

a grate + full + ly = _____

b converse + ation + ally = _____

c energy + etic + ally = _____

d photograph + ic + ally = _____

e thank + full + ly = _____

f joy + full + ly = _____

g horrify + ic + ally = _____

h respect + full + ly = _____

**2** Pick two different suffixes from the box that can be added to each of these words. The first one has been done for you.

a correct      correct _ion_____      correct _ly_____

b product      product_____      product_____

c construct      construct_____      construct_____

d extreme      extreme_____      extreme_____

e act      act_____      act_____

f real      real_____      real_____

g oppress      oppress_____      oppress_____

h miss      miss_____      miss_____

| |
|---|
| ive |
| ly |
| ion |
| ist |

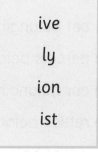

# Rhyming patterns

Poets use rhyme in different ways.

Some poems have **alternate rhyming lines**.

Some lines rhyme in pairs. These are called **rhyming couplets**.

Some poems use **no rhyme** at all.

Snow falls,
Wind blows,
Bird calls,
Hungry crows.

Sunny days,
Warm rays,
Burning down,
Grass brown.

Rain splashes,
Wet feet,
Dripping trees,
Black puddles.

**1** Write whether each poem has alternate rhyming lines, rhyming couplets or no rhyme.

a

Black night,

Halloween fright,

Bright moon,

A silver balloon.

This poem has

_____

_____

b

Green trees,

Spring leaves,

Fresh-cut grass,

Crunchy apples.

This poem has

_____

_____

c

Red nose,

Warm scarf,

Rosy glows,

Cosy hearth.

This poem has

_____

_____

**2** Add two lines to each of these poems, making sure you match the rhyming patterns.

a Packed bags,

Luggage tags,

Clutching passport,

Crowded airport,

_____

_____

b Christmas tree,

Gifts below,

Treats for me,

There on show,

_____

_____

# Making notes

When we make notes, we only need to write down the **key words**.

**1** Underline the key words in each sentence.

a Molly and Sam are coming to tea.

b I have gone for lunch, but I will be back at noon.

c My birthday is in December.

d Remember you are playing football on Saturday.

e I have Maths and English homework to do.

f We need to buy some milk and bread.

**2** Write a full sentence for each set of notes.

a Tea in oven.

_____

b Brownies, Town Hall, 6pm.

_____

c Lucy's party, Friday, buy gift.

_____

d In garden, come round back.

_____

e Mum rang. Running late.

_____

f Car fixed. Please collect.

_____

# Prefixes

Prefixes are letter strings added to the beginning of root words to **change** their **meaning**. Here are some examples of prefixes and their meanings.

| | |
|---|---|
| *re* back, again | *super* above |
| *sub* under | *anti* against |
| *inter* between, among | *auto* self, own |

**1** Use the prefixes to help you write the meanings of these words. If you do not know the words, look them up in the dictionary.

a international _____

b remake _____

c automobile _____

d submarine _____

e antidote _____

f replay _____

g superior _____

**2** Draw a line to match each prefix to its correct ending.

a re                 standard

b sub                place

c inter              biotics

d re                 val

e anti               vise

f super              veal

g auto               mobile

# Nouns and pronouns

Pronouns help to make writing flow more easily. If you used nouns all of the time, you just repeat yourself.

The dog walked into the garden. The dog jumped up at the fence and barked, and then the dog lapped up some water.

The dog walked into the garden. **She** jumped up at the fence and barked, and then **she** lapped up some water.

**1** **Change the repeated nouns to pronouns. Rewrite the sentences.**

a The cat likes milk. The cat drinks it regularly.

_____

b Birds fly into our garden. The birds like our pond.

_____

c A man walked along the beach. The man picked up shells.

_____

d The women were running. The women were keeping fit.

_____

**2** **Write five sentences using a noun and a pronoun each time.**

a _____

b _____

c _____

d _____

e _____

# Punctuating speech

When using inverted commas (or speech marks), we have to follow some rules about punctuation and capital letters.

Sometimes we write who is speaking before we write what they say.

*Attia said, "Let's go and play!"*

Put a comma before the inverted commas. The full stop, question mark or exclamation mark at the end of the sentence goes inside the inverted commas.

Sometimes we write what they say first, then write who is speaking.

*"Great, let's go," said Mari.*

The first word of a piece of speech always starts with a capital letter.

A comma, question mark or exclamation mark at the end of the speech is used inside the inverted commas.

---

**1** Look carefully at this piece of writing. Circle the mistakes that have been made with inverted commas, punctuation and capital letters.

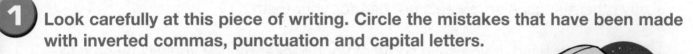

"Stop! Thief"! yelled the shopkeeper.

Max asked, "what's the matter?"

"That man stole the money from the till, replied the shopkeeper."

Max asked", Which way did he go?"

The shopkeeper said, "Over the bridge towards the station".

"I'll follow him, and you phone the police", shouted Max.

"You can't escape", panted Max as he ran after the thief.

'You'll never catch me!," replied the thief.

**2** Add inverted commas and punctuation to these sentences.

a Wesley   said   We're   going   to   Spain   on   holiday

b Can   I   have   a   drink   please   asked   Lola

c Ouch   yelled   Kira

d Luke   asked   What   time   is   it

e My   big   brother   shouted   Get   out

# Balanced arguments

A balanced argument needs to include both points of view.

Connectives like *if*, *also*, *then*, *although*, *however* and *on the other hand*, allow us to compare different points of view.

I think swimming is the best sport. Kelly, **on the other hand**, loves tennis.

**1** Underline the connectives in this argument.

If you spend all your pocket money on sweets, then you will not have any left to buy other things. Also, sweets are bad for your teeth.

On the other hand, if you save some of your pocket money you will be able to buy something you really want. Although it can take a while to save enough, it will be worth it in the end.

**2** Here is an argument about whether children should be allowed to choose when they go to bed. Pick connectives from the box to complete the argument.

| if | then | on the other hand | however | although | also |
|----|------|-------------------|---------|----------|------|

_____ children know how tired they feel, they are too young to understand how much sleep they really need. _____ children are allowed to decide when they go to bed, _____ they may be too tired to concentrate at school. _____, tired children can be very bad-tempered, which could cause arguments at home.

_____, being able to choose their own bedtimes may actually save arguments in the family. Children can always catch up with sleep at the weekends. _____, this would use up a lot of their free time.

# Alliteration

Alliteration is when several words next to each other, or very close together, begin with the **same sound**.

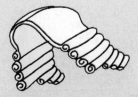

one white wig

bright blue balloon

Using alliteration draws attention to that part of your writing and helps to add rhythm, especially in poetry.

**1** Underline the alliteration in each sentence.

a Daisy danced daintily across the stage.

b Crystal the cat crept cautiously to the door.

c Katie bought a pink patterned purse.

d Philip found frogs in the pond.

e Noble knights never run from battle.

f Gemma tells tall tales.

g Rachel's rabbits wriggled in her arms.

h Nasty gnomes never play fair.

**2** Finish each phrase by adding two more words that start with the same sound.

a beautiful babies _____ _____

b tall trees _____ _____

c honest ogres _____ _____

d sleepy Simon _____ _____

e careful Cara _____ _____

f fat fairies _____ _____

g poor Peter _____ _____

h reckless rhinos _____ _____

# The *g* sound spelt *gue* and the *k* sound spelt *que*

English has lots of French words and spellings as part of the language. These spellings can be tricky, so it is a pattern you just have to learn and remember.

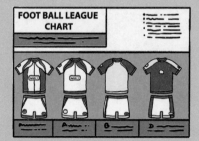

league

mosque

**1** Learn these spellings using the LOOK, COVER, WRITE, CHECK method.

a league _____     d plague _____

b tongue _____     e rogue _____

c fatigue _____

Write other words that use the pattern gue for the g sound.

_____

**2** Learn these spellings using the LOOK, COVER, WRITE, CHECK method. Write a sentence for each word to show you understand the meaning.

a antique _____

b unique _____

c mosque _____

d cheque _____

e opaque _____

Write other words that use the pattern que for the k sound.

_____

## *Its* and *it's*

Apostrophes are used to **shorten** and **join** words together.

**It is** my parrot ➡ **It's** my parrot

They also show when something belongs to someone.

Sian**'s** parrot.

These are called possessive apostrophes. The only exception is *it*, which never has a possessive apostrophe.

The parrot flapped **its** wings.

**1** Add the apostrophe to *its* in these sentences if it is necessary.

a The cat licked its paws.

b Its my favourite book.

c Its starting to rain.

d The hamster escaped from its cage.

e In the autumn the tree loses its leaves.

f Its easier to roller-skate than ice-skate.

g The dog wagged its tail.

**2** Rewrite these sentences, replacing the words in bold with *its* or *it's*.

a I like popcorn, because **it is** sweet and crunchy.

_____

b **It is** important to take care when you cross the road.

_____

c The bird flapped **the bird's** wings.

_____

d **It is** hot today.

_____

e When **the clock's** battery ran down, the clock stopped working.

_____

f The flower opened **the flower's** petals.

_____

# ANSWERS

**Page 2**
1. Make sure your child can ask questions about schools in the past, and listen carefully to the answers. Encourage your child to think about a variety of topics such as school subjects, food, playtimes and friends.
2. Make sure your child can write an account of the interview that looks at similarities and differences between schools in the past, when the interviewee was at school, and the present day.

**Page 3**
1. a new
   b whole
   c great
   d their
   e too or to
   f heard
   g see
   h bee
   i four or fore
   j right or rite
2. Any sentences that show your child understands the words given.

**Page 4**
1. a jumping
   b preferred
   c kicks
   d grabbed
   e gardening
   f saved, saving
   g lifts, lifting
2. a stopped
   b limited
   c carried
   d washes
   e began
   f explores

**Page 5**
1. a merriment
   b kindness
   c fitness
   d enjoyment
   e laziness
   f membership
   g silliness
   h friendship
   i carelessness
   j happiness
2. a measurement
   b tidiness
   c nastiness
   d employment
   e statement
   f wickedness
   g fellowship
   h apprenticeship
   i replacement
   j championship

**Page 6**
1. Chat with your child about their favourite film. Make sure they understand the questions, and how much detail to give in their answers.
   a Title of a favourite film.
   b Explanation of why the favourite character is a favourite.
   c An opinion, backed up with reasons, about the most exciting part of the film.
   d An opinion given about the ending, with mention of any problems that have been resolved.
2. a Any 'day out' place mentioned and reason for going (i.e. 'to see the waterfall'; 'to look at sculptures').
   b Description of the journey.
   c Description of the events of the day.
   d Opinion about whether the child would like to repeat the day out.
   e Opinion on whether the day out was good enough to be recommended to a friend.

**Page 7**
1. a submarine
   b success
   c sudden
   d sugar
   e suitable
   f summer
   g sunny
   h super
   i suspect
2. a hail
   b hair
   c hard
   d hare
   e harp
   f haste
   g hat
   h have

**Page 8**
1. a completely
   b comically
   c usually
   d sleepily
   e badly
   f totally
   g humbly
   h basically
   i gently
2. Any suitable adverb that makes a sensible sentence.

**Page 9**
1. a deepen
   b shorten
   c standardise
   d apologise
   e notify
   f elasticate
   g purify
   h formalise
   i waken
   j medicate
2. a intensify
   b realise
   c strengthen
   d simplify
   e harden
   f glorify
   g hasten
   h classify
   i serialise
   j weaken

**Page 10**
1. a hurt
   b put
   c ran
   d brought
   e sent
   f fell
2. a Yesterday, I ate my birthday cake.
   b Last week, Jamilla bought a comic.
   c Earlier today, Ali drew a picture.
   d Last night, I was tired.
   e When I was four, I could swim.
   f Yesterday, I told you a secret.

**Page 11**
1. a After tea, we played football.
   b Find your trainers, Paul.
   c Suddenly, the lights went out.
   d Judy and James, from next door, came shopping with us.
   e My hat, which is black, matches my scarf.
   f Last Tuesday, after school, I went skating.
2. a Tomorrow, we are playing football.
   b The ink, which was blue, stained the carpet.
   c Eventually, Jane won the game.
   d It's time to go, Ali.
   e While we were on holiday, we stayed in a hotel.
   f At school, in my classroom, is a display about trains.

**Page 12**
1. a hobbles   b argues   c devours
   shuffles   dictates   munches
   ambles   declares   chews
   Accept any additional verbs that are suitable.
2. The powerful verbs should appear in the following order in the story: ordered, yelled, shot, clambered, crept, gazed, grabbed, fled, hacked, crashed

**Page 13**
1. a she ate her breakfast.
   b he waited for his lunch.
   c he watched the stars.
   d I'll make lots of festive cakes and biscuits.
   e the hedgehog slept.
   f he packed his bags.
   g she watched out of the window.
2. Any sensible fronted adverbial followed by a comma.

**Page 14**
1. a while
   b before
   c after
   d soon
   e during
2. Any sentences which contain the adverb, conjunction or preposition given, and make sense.

**Page 15**
1. a sniffs
   b halves
   c puffs
   d cliffs
   e scarves
   f scuffs
   g calves
   h thieves
   i yourselves
   j knives
2. a loaves
   b selves
   c sheriffs
   d cuffs
   e wolves
   f wives
   g bluffs
   h shelves
   i elves
   j scoffs

**Page 16**
1. a starving
   b exhausted
   c lovely
   d horrible
   e terrifying
   f parched
   g drenched
   h hilarious
2. Many answers are possible. Any sensible choice of exciting words for each sentence

**Page 17**
1. Any more exciting, expanded sentence for each question in the style of the example.
2. Any interesting, descriptive sentences using each of the nouns given.